NO PLACE LIKE

Home

BY KNIT PICKS

Photography by Amy Cave

Printed in the United States of America

First Printing, 2016

ISBN 978-1-62767-132-3

Versa Press, Inc
800-447-7829

www.versapress.com

To Theo. May you grow up with a love for all God's creatures.
— K B H

May you be friends with animals, taking them into your family with a good and giving heart:
your faithfulness to them will bless both you and the world around you.
— A S

KATHERINE BOLGER HYDE has devoted her life to books as a reader, editor, and writer. Her works include the picture books *Lucia, Saint of Light* (AFP, 2009) and *Everything Tells Us about God* (AFP, 2018); the young adult fantasy *The Dome-Singer of Falenda*; and the adult mystery series Crime with the Classics. Katherine lives in the redwood country of the California central coast, where she shares a home with two domesticated humans and two wild and crazy cats.

ANASTASIYA SOKOLOVA is an artist, designer, illustrator, and teacher who lives and works in Moscow with her husband, four children, and a good-natured cat. Trained as an architect, Anastasia built a cozy wooden house with her own hands in the Russian outback, the interior of which she also designed and decorated with her own paintings. She began illustrating books in 2012. *A Taste of Paradise* is her first book in English.

A Taste of Paradise

Text copyright © 2022 Katherine Bolger Hyde • Illustrations copyright © 2022 Anastasiya Sokolova
Reprinted in 2022

ANCIENT FAITH PUBLISHING
A division of Ancient Faith Ministries
PO Box 748 • Chesterton, IN 46304

ISBN 978-1-955890-10-6 • Library of Congress Control Number 2022932985

store.ancientfaith.com

PRINTED IN CANADA

These saints are not so very different from you.

You may have a puppy or kitten,

A bird or a fish or a hamster,

And you love it and care for all its needs.

When you show love and kindness to an animal—

Wild or tame, fierce or friendly, little or big—

You are helping to restore our world

To the way God first intended it to be.

You are creating a little taste of Paradise.

Saint Paisius lived on Mount Athos not so very long ago.

He made friends there with many wild creatures,

Jackals, hares, and ferrets, turtles, lizards, and snakes.

But his favorite was a little bird he called Olet.

Olet would eat worms from Paisius's hand,

But he came not only for food; he came for friendship too.

Olet would fly to Paisius whenever he called.

One day the saint left food for the bird without seeing him,

And the next day Olet flew to meet him, crazy with joy.

"My little friend," said Paisius, "let us praise the Lord together!"

Saint Cuthbert lived as a hermit, all alone

On the isle of Farne in the cold North Sea.

The birds and beasts were his only companions.

Each night Cuthbert would wade into the sea

And stand up to his waist in the frigid waters to pray.

In the morning, two otters would come to him

And lie on his feet to warm them with their thick, glossy fur.

When he had thawed, they would stay to play,

Splashing and frolicking in the shallow waters,

And then at last, they'd catch some fish to share with

    Cuthbert for breakfast.

Saint Jerome sat in his cell in Bethlehem,

Translating the sacred Scriptures,

When a mournful cry rumbled through

    the earth at his feet.

At the door of his cell sat a mighty lion,

Brought low by a sharp thorn stuck deep in its paw.

"Let me help you, brother," said Jerome to the lion

As he pulled out the thorn and tended to

    the wound.

The lion licked his hand, lay down at his feet,

    and refused to leave.

From that day on, the lion earned his keep

    by guarding a donkey

And carrying wood and water on his broad,

    strong back.

Everyone must work in a monastery!

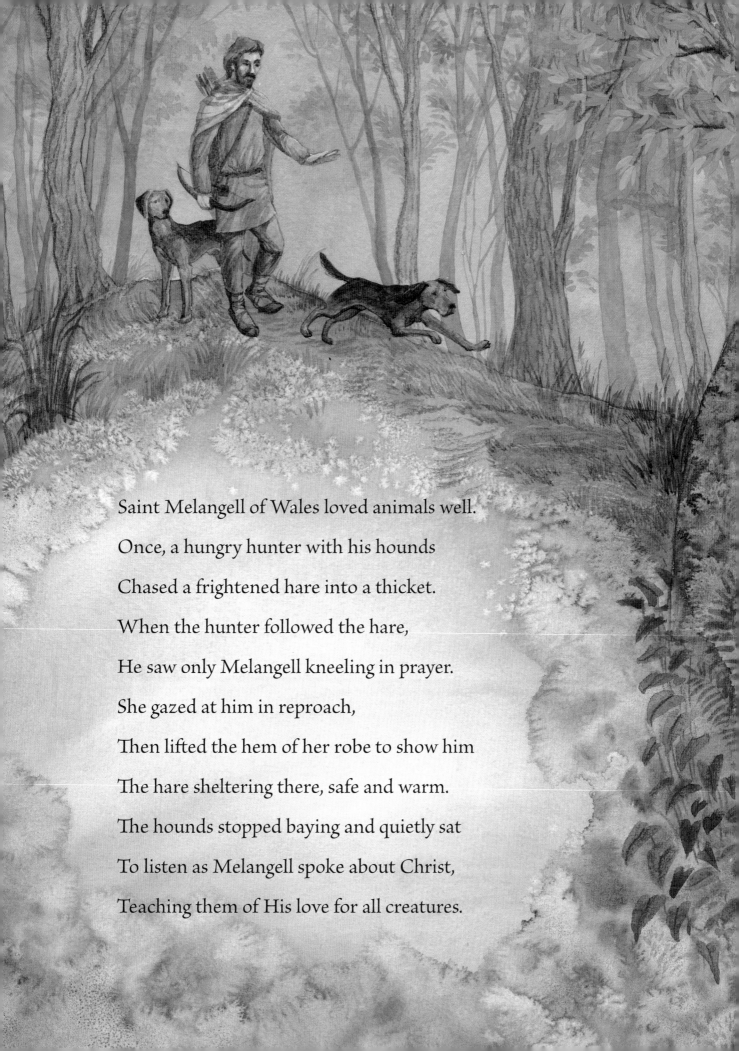

Saint Melangell of Wales loved animals well.

Once, a hungry hunter with his hounds

Chased a frightened hare into a thicket.

When the hunter followed the hare,

He saw only Melangell kneeling in prayer.

She gazed at him in reproach,

Then lifted the hem of her robe to show him

The hare sheltering there, safe and warm.

The hounds stopped baying and quietly sat

To listen as Melangell spoke about Christ,

Teaching them of His love for all creatures.

Saint John of San Francisco had a wild dove for his friend.

The dove first came to him with an injured wing,

And John splinted the wing so it would heal.

For the rest of his life, the dove would visit Saint John,

Who called it Gulya and let it fly freely around his home.

The two would have long conversations,

And people said Gulya brought messages from God.

When Saint John blessed the waters at Theophany,

Gulya swooped over the water again and again,

As if bearing the blessing of the Holy Spirit in its wings.

Saint Kieran of Ireland journeyed deep into the woods

To build himself a cell where he could pray in peace.

Gathering wood was hard work, and soon he grew weary.

As he rested under a tree, a wild boar thundered near

With blazing red fire in its eyes, brandishing vicious tusks.

Kieran said, "Brother Boar, I have no wish to harm you.

Let us be friends, and use your tusks for better work."

The boar bowed its head in submission,

Then got to work tearing down branches,

Which Kieran used to build his cell.

In time many other beasts came to join the boar,

And Kieran called them his brother monks.

Saint Mary of Egypt lived forty years in the desert,

And in all that time the wild beasts left her in peace,

Perhaps sensing she was precious to God.

When she died, her friend Zossima wanted to bury her,

But the parched ground was like iron and he had no tools.

In despair, he cried out to God to help him bury the saint.

Then a lion appeared out of the wilderness.

Zossima trembled in fear, but seeing the lion looked friendly,

He said, "O brother beast, will you help me dig this grave?"

Within minutes the lion's sharp claws had hollowed out the ground.

When Zossima had reverently laid Mary's body to rest,

the lion filled in the grave and

peacefully went his way.

Saint Seraphim of Sarov lived deep in the Russian forest,

In a small hut sheltered by birch trees,

All alone except for his animal friends.

With them he shared his morsel of daily bread.

Deer and rabbits, foxes and squirrels all came to eat together,

But Seraphim's favorite friend was a bear called Misha.

Each day Misha would lie down at Seraphim's feet

And use his giant rough tongue

To lick the bread out of the holy man's hand.

No matter how many animals hopped or scurried

or ran to the hut for dinner,

There was always enough bread for all—

And a little for Seraphim, too.

The Lord told Elijah to hide by a brook from the wrath of the king,

And there He sent ravens to feed him.

Morning and evening the ravens came,

In their strong talons bearing bread and meat,

Which they laid at the prophet's feet, then received his blessing.

Elijah drank from the brook, and so the Lord sustained him.

Elijah the Prophet served the Lord well

In a time when all Israel had betrayed Him.

At the Lord's command, Elijah proclaimed a drought

Would fall on the land to punish the wicked king Ahab.

Saint Mamas the Great Martyr was walking through the desert

When he spied a fearsome lion attacking a little lamb.

Mamas left his path and raced up to the lion,

And with his stick he smacked it on the nose.

"Lion, leave your weaker brother alone!" he cried.

The lion retreated and bowed its head in shame.

Mamas took the trembling lamb gently in his arms

And mounted the lordly lion as if it were a horse.

The humbled lion carried them into town,

Where all were amazed at the sight of

    lion, monk, and lamb

Traveling together in harmony.

Saint Herman of Alaska lived alone on a tiny island

Battered both winter and summer by storms and waves.

Some ermines—bad-tempered creatures

    with fierce, sharp teeth—

Gave birth to their babies under his hut,

And each day he would feed them by hand.

The mothers never nipped him or hissed at him

As he stroked their babies' soft white fur.

Even the huge and frightening Kodiak bears

Would bow their heads to Herman and be fed,

For they knew he was God's good friend.

Saint Brigid of Ireland loved sheep and cattle,

And not only for the wool and milk they gave.

Her heart had room for wild beasts as well.

Once she offered sanctuary to a wild boar

So that hunters would not kill him.

Another time, she tamed a fox and gave it as pet to a king.

Once she visited a family whose cow had stopped giving milk,

So they would have to kill the cow for meat.

In pity for man and beast, she blessed the cow,

and its milk overflowed the buckets

for the rest of its life.

Saint Modestos ruled the church in Jerusalem.

His heart was full of love for all God's creatures.

A poor widow begged him in prayer for help with her oxen,

Her only livelihood, who all lay sick and dying.

In a dream he told her, "Do not fear.

Have a cross forged of iron cut from one of your tools,

Dip the cross in holy oil, and bless your beasts."

She obeyed his word, and they were healed.

Now we pray to Saint Modestos

      as the patron saint of animals.

Long ago in Paradise,

Animals and men walked side by side.

Big, fierce creatures velveted their claws

And gently played with those more small and meek.

Love reigned among all God's creatures.

None had any cause to be afraid.

God has promised us that one day, when Christ reigns,

All His creatures once again will live in peace.

And even now, while Earth is still in darkness,

Holy men and women, full of Light,

Bear God's love to all those He created—

To people and to animals, tame and wild.

Let's meet some of these lovers of God's creatures

And see their Spirit-filled

    friendships come to life.

A Taste
of
Paradise

STORIES OF SAINTS
AND ANIMALS

Katherine Bolger Hyde
Illustrated by Anastasiya Sokolova

ANCIENT FAITH
PUBLISHING

CHESTERTON, INDIANA